HANDS-ON WORDS

FUN FILL-INS

by Marilynn G. Barr

Jack and Jill went up the hill to fetch a pail of ____.

Publisher: Roberta Suid

Production: Little Acorn & Associates, Inc.

MM2202
FUN FILL-INS
Entire contents copyright © 2005
by Monday Morning Books, Inc.

For a complete catalog, write to the address below:
Monday Morning Books, Inc.
PO Box 1134
Inverness, CA 94937

Call our toll-free number: 1-800-255-6049
E-mail us at: MMBooks@aol.com
Visit our Web site:
http://www.mondaymorningbooks.com
For more products featuring art by Marilynn G. Barr visit www.littleacornbooks.com

ISBN 1-57612-254-9

Printed in the United States of America
9 8 7 6 5 4 3 2 1

Contents

Introduction

Make early reading a thrill with *Fun Fill-ins*. Children giggle as they develop early literacy and reasoning skills when they transform familiar stories into funny tales. Jack and Jill fetch a pail of alligators! Yankee Doodle sticks a cow in his hat! The owl and the pussycat go to sea in a beautiful pea green shoe. Contents include popular poems, songs, rhymes, and stories. Activities feature fill-in-the-blank story boards with cutout picture and word stickers. Beginning word cards, games, rewards, and project ideas are also included. Games and word cards offer beginning sound, word recognition, memory, and matching skills practice. Children can use writing boards to practice writing words found in each story. Projects provide fine motor and early word skills practice.

Fill-in the Blanks Story Boards

Each story includes fill-in-the-blank story boards and picture word stamps for children to transform familiar stories into <u>funny</u> tales. Choose a story to read to the children. Then have children recite it with you. Reproduce the matching set of funny fill-in story boards for each child to color and cut out. Children then cut out and glue a silly picture word on the board to complete the phrase or sentence. Help children write matching words under each picture word. Provide construction paper for children to make covers for their books. Invite children, in turn, to read their "Fun Fill-ins" to the other children for lots of laughter. Children can also draw their own silly pictures in the squares. Stories can also be done correctly.

Flannel Board Stories

Cover a large sheet of corrugated board with blue felt or other fabric that works well with Velcro. Provide each child with a set of construction paper character and prop patterns for each story. Have children color and cut out the patterns. Help each child glue a Velcro square to the back of each of his or her patterns. Children can tell flannel board stories using the characters and props during individual or group play—the sillier the story, the better!

Story Collages

Provide each child with a large sheet of construction paper and a set of patterns from a story. Have children color, cut out, arrange, then glue the patterns on a sheet of construction paper. Provide assorted craft materials for children to finish decorating their collages. Fold and attach a length of masking tape (front to back) along each edge to form a frame. Children can use permanent markers to decorate the masking tape frames. Display finished collages.

Fun Fill-ins Traveling Story Pockets

Prepare a work station for children to make traveling pockets from large envelopes to carry fill-in story boards, stamps, and patterns. Have children decorate their envelopes. Reproduce each set of story patterns, fill-in story boards, and stamps for each child to color and cut out. Provide craft sticks and glue for children to attach to the backs of story patterns to form puppets. Children can take their traveling story pockets home to share with friends and family.

Double-sided Story Wands

Reproduce, color, cut out, and glue identical story patterns on each outside panel of a folder. Staple the top and long, open side of the folder. Glue a paint stirrer inside the center of the remaining open side of the folder to form a handle for the "Story Wand." Staple the open edges on either side of the stirrer to reinforce it. Double-sided story wands are perfect for reading circles. (Children can see the words as you read.)

Back

Front

Word Cards

Word cards (pp. 54-61) can be used to play a game of Concentration. Reproduce, cut apart, and glue two sets of word cards on index cards. You can also color-code word cards to differentiate sight words, picture words, and so on. Store cards or card sets in decorated and labeled checkbook boxes. Resealable plastic bags are also convenient storage containers.

The Man in the Moon

The man in the moon
looked out of the moon.
He looked out of the moon and said,
"It's time for all children on earth
to get ready for bed!"

MM2202 • Fun Fill-ins • ©2005 Monday Morning Books, Inc.

The Man in the Moon

The Man in the Moon

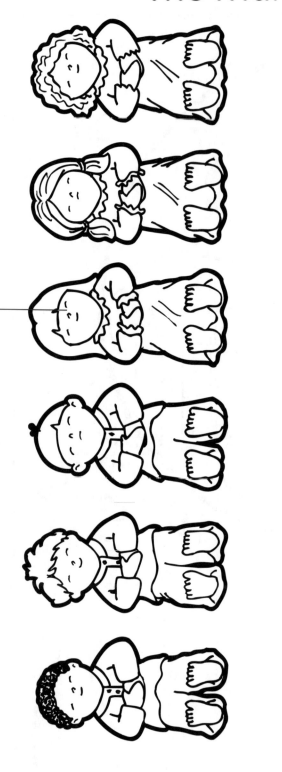

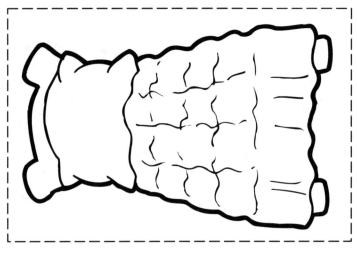

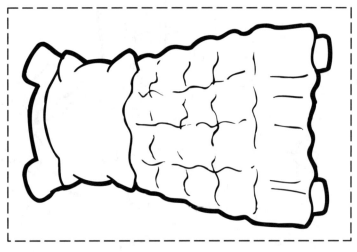

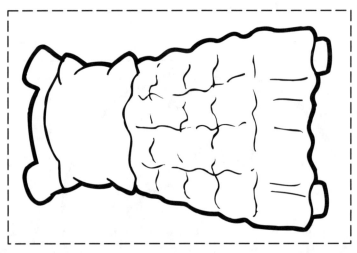

Reproduce sleeping children and two sets of beds for each child to color, cut out, and glue on a sheet of construction paper.

MM2202 • Fun Fill-ins • ©2005 Monday Morning Books, Inc.

The Man in the Moon Story Board

Name _____

The ⌐ ¬ in the moon
    ⌊ _ ⌋

_____
Write the matching word here.

looked out of the moon.

horse

man

cow

shoe

Read the words.
Cut out and glue a picture in the square.
Write the matching word in the space provided.

The Man in the Moon Story Board

Name _____

He looked out of the

Write the matching word here.

and said,

tub   shoe   moon   box

Read the words.
Cut out and glue a picture in the square.
Write the matching word in the space provided.

MM2202 • Fun Fill-ins • ©2005 Monday Morning Books, Inc.

The Man in the Moon Story Board

Name _____

"It's time for all [ ] on earth

_____
Write the matching word here.

horses

elephants

children

pretzels

Read the words.
Cut out and glue a picture in the square.
Write the matching word in the space provided.

The Man in the Moon Story Board

Name _____

to get ready for  .

_____
Write the matching word here.

bed   brooms   umbrellas   turtles

Read the words.
Cut out and glue a picture in the square.
Write the matching word in the space provided.

MM2202 • Fun Fill-ins • ©2005 Monday Morning Books, Inc.

Moon Walkers

Materials: folder, construction paper, crayons, markers, scissors, glue, large buttons, envelope

Reproduce, color, and cut out the "Moon Walkers" game board patterns. Matching at the center, glue the game board patterns to the inside of a folder. Decorate and write "Moon Walkers" on the front of the folder. Reproduce, color, laminate, then cut apart two sets of game cards. (These cards can also be used to play a game of Concentration.) To play: Shuffle and place the game cards on the table face down. In turn, each player picks a card, identifies the beginning sound letter, and moves his or her button pawn to the matching letter space. Play continues until all players reach The End. When all cards have been played, reshuffle and place the cards in a draw pile to continue play. Make additional picture word cards for children to practice identifying more beginning sound letters. Store cards and pawns inside an envelope taped to the back of the folder.

Moon Walkers Game Board

Moon Walkers Game Board

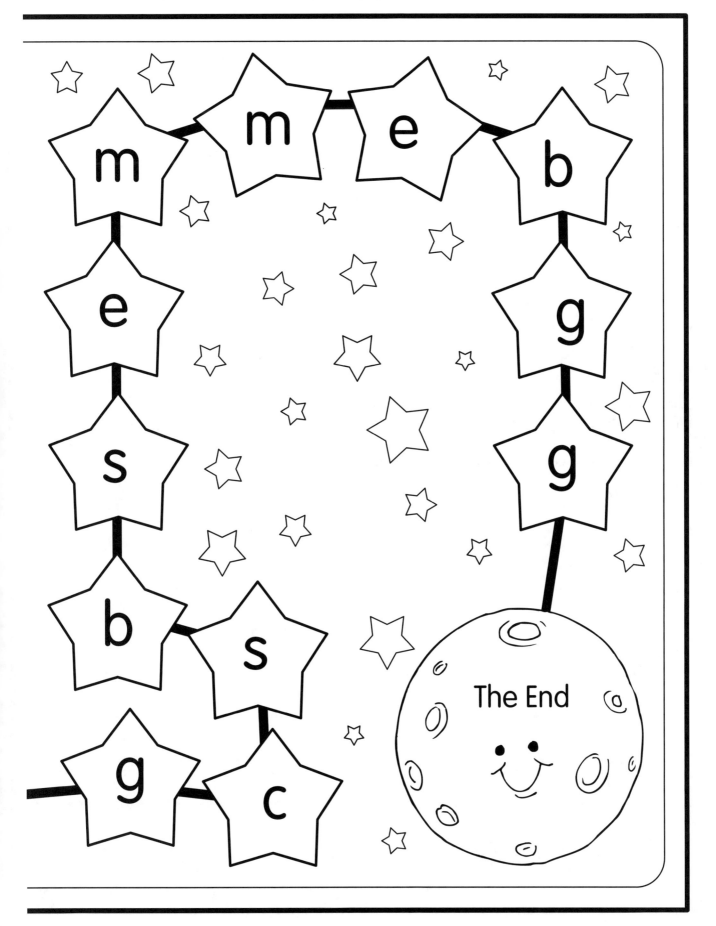

The End

The Man in the Moon Writing Boards

Name _____

_____

_____

_____

_____

_____

Name _____

_____

_____

_____

_____

_____

_____

MM2202 • Fun Fill-ins • ©2005 Monday Morning Books, Inc.

Jack and Jill

Jack and Jill
went up the hill
to fetch a pail of water.
Jack fell down
and broke his crown,
and Jill came tumbling after.

Jack and Jill

Pail

Jack

Provide children with crayons, markers, and scissors to color and cut out the patterns. Have children glue craft sticks to the backs of patterns to make stick puppets.

MM2202 • Fun Fill-ins • ©2005 Monday Morning Books, Inc.

Jack and Jill

Jill

Pail

Provide children with crayons, markers, and scissors to color and cut out the patterns. Have children glue craft sticks to the backs of patterns to make stick puppets.

Jack and Jill Story Board

Name _____

Jack and Jill

went ⬚ the hill

_____
Write the matching word here.

up   down

Read the words.
Cut out and glue a picture in the square.
Write the matching word in the space provided.

Jack and Jill Story Board

Name _____

to fetch a pail of

_____
Write the matching word here.

Read the words.
Cut out and glue a
picture in the square.
Write the matching
word in the space
provided.

pigs

turtles

water

bees

alligators

kittens

Jack and Jill Story Board

Name _____

Jack fell down

and broke his ⬚ ,

_____
Write the matching word here.

crown   cup   pillow   pretzel

Read the words.
Cut out and glue a picture in the square.
Write the matching word in the space provided.

MM2202 • Fun Fill-ins • ©2005 Monday Morning Books, Inc.

Jack and Jill Story Board

Name _____

and ⬚ came

_____
Write the matching word here.

tumbling after.

pigs

turtles

Jill

Read the words.
Cut out and glue a picture in the square.
Write the matching word in the space provided.

bees

alligators

kittens

Jack and Jill Writing Boards

Name _____

Name _____

MM2202 • Fun Fill-ins • ©2005 Monday Morning Books, Inc.

What's in your pail?

Materials: large envelope, construction paper, crayons, markers, scissors, glue, pawns

Reproduce, color, cut out, and glue the "What's in you pail?" game board to the front of a large envelope. Reproduce, color, laminate, then cut apart two sets of game cards. These cards can also be used to play a game of "Concentration." To play: Shuffle and place the game cards on the table face down. In turn, each player picks a card and identifies the beginning sound letter that matches the picture. If correct, the player moves his or her pawn forward one space and the next player takes a turn. If incorrect, the player does not move forward. Play continues until all players reach The End. When all cards have been played, reshuffle and place the cards in a draw pile to continue play. Make additional picture word cards for children to practice identifying more beginning sound letters. Store cards and pawns inside the envelope.

What's in your pail? Game Board

What's in your pail?

Start

The End

MM2202 • Fun Fill-ins • ©2005 Monday Morning Books, Inc.

The Owl and the Pussycat

The owl and the pussycat went to sea
in a beautiful pea green boat.
They took some honey
and plenty of money
wrapped up in a five pound note.

The Owl and the Pussycat

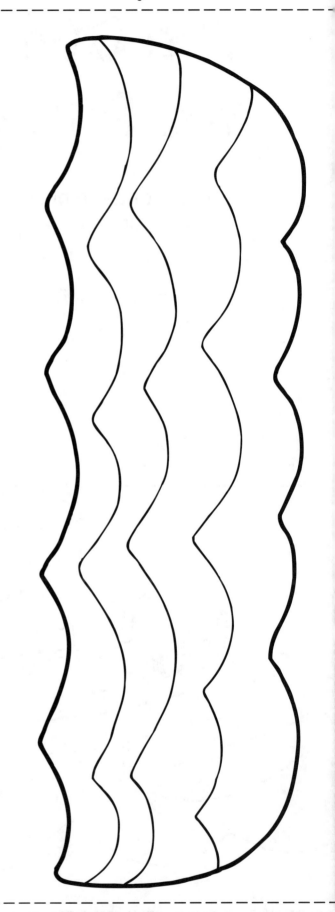

Provide children with crayons, markers, and scissors to color and cut out the patterns. Have children glue craft sticks to the backs of patterns to make stick puppets.

The Owl and the Pussycat

The Owl and the Pussycat Story Board

Name _____

The owl and the pussycat

went to sea

in a beautiful pea green _____ .

_____
Write the matching word here.

sandbox

umbrella

pool

Read the words.
Cut out and glue a
picture in the
square.
Write the matching
word in the space
provided.

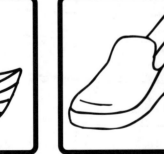

boat

shoe

cup

MM2202 • Fun Fill-ins • ©2005 Monday Morning Books, Inc.

The Owl and the Pussycat Story Board

Name _____

They took some

_____
Write the matching word here.

and plenty of money

wrapped up in a five pound note.

bunnies

elephants

puppies

Read the words.
Cut out and glue a
picture in the
square.
Write the matching
word in the space
provided.

honey

ladybugs

carrots

The Owl and the Pussycat Writing Boards

Name _____

_____

- -

_____

Name _____

_____

- -

_____

  MM2202 • Fun Fill-ins • ©2005 Monday Morning Books, Inc.

Sailing, Sailing

Materials: large envelopes, construction paper, crayons, markers, scissors, glue

Program "Sailing, Sailing" lotto boards with different combinations of the following beginning sound letters: h, c, e, s, u, l, p, d, b, o. Reproduce a lotto board and a set of cards for each child to color. Have each child cut out and glue his or her board to the front of an envelope. Laminate and cut apart each child's set of cards. To play: Have children place their sailboat lotto boards and cards, face up, on their desks. Call out "I see something that begins with a "c" on my sail. What's on my sail?" Instruct children to choose and place a lotto card that begins with a "c" on their sails. Play continues until every child has filled up his or her sail. Then invite each child, in turn, to tell what is on his or her sail.

Sailing, Sailing Game Board

MM2202 • Fun Fill-ins • ©2005 Monday Morning Books, Inc.

There Was an Old Woman

There was an old woman
who lived in a shoe.
She had so many children
She did not know what to do.
She gave them some soup
and a slice of brown bread.
Then she hugged them and
put them to bed.

There Was an Old Woman

Put the Kids to Bed

Reproduce and color 26 children and bed patterns.
Program the children with lowercase letters and the
beds with uppercase letters. Laminate, then cut
apart the patterns. Write "Put the Kids to Bed" on the
front of a large envelope. Then glue an old woman
pattern under the title. Children match upper and
lowercase patterns. Store cutouts in the envelope
when not in use.

 MM2202 • Fun Fill-ins • ©2005 Monday Morning Books, Inc.

There Was an Old Woman

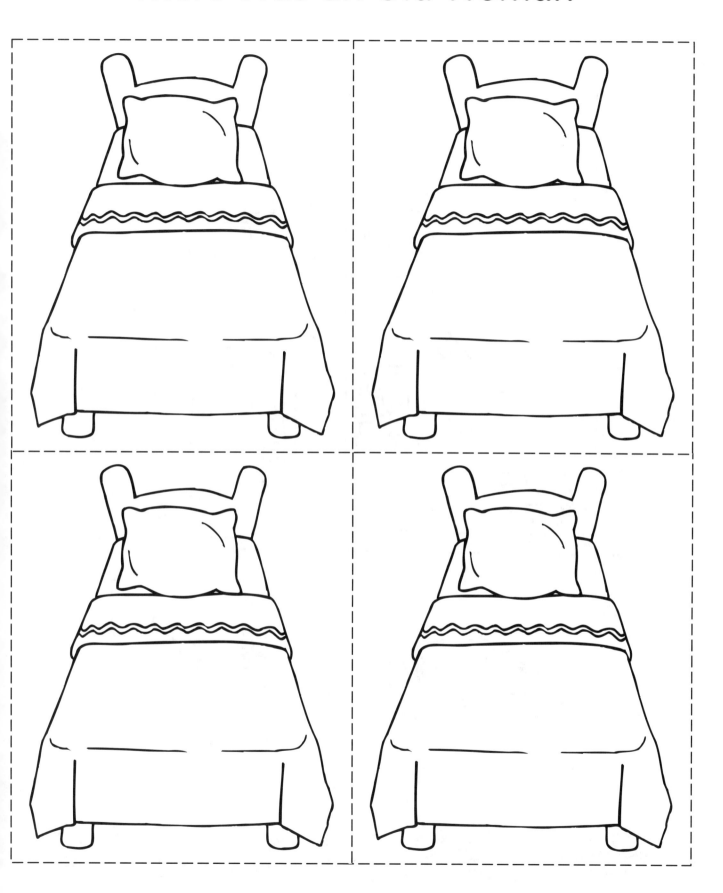

There Was an Old Woman

 MM2202 • Fun Fill-ins • ©2005 Monday Morning Books, Inc.

There Was an Old Woman Story Board

Name _____

There was an old woman

who lived in a  .

_____
Write the matching word here.

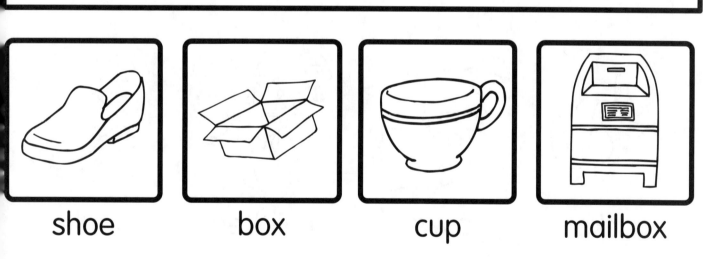

shoe   box   cup   mailbox

Read the words.
Cut out and glue a picture in the square.
Write the matching word in the space provided.

There Was an Old Woman Story Board

Name _____

She had so many

_____
Write the matching word here.

She did not know what to do.

ducks

cows

children

turtles

Read the words.
Cut out and glue a picture in the square.
Write the matching word in the space provided.

MM2202 • Fun Fill-ins • ©2005 Monday Morning Books, Inc.

There Was an Old Woman Story Board

Name _____

She gave them some

Write the matching word here.

and a slice of brown bread.

dogs

elephants

soup

frogs

Read the words.
Cut out and glue a picture in the square.
Write the matching word in the space provided.

There Was an Old Woman Story Board

Name _____

She hugged them and put

them to [   ] .

_____
Write the matching word here.

bed

fiddle

slide

Read the words.
Cut out and glue a picture in the square.
Write the matching word in the space provided.

MM2202 • Fun Fill-ins • ©2005 Monday Morning Books, Inc.

There Was an Old Woman Writing Boards

Name _____

Name _____

Going Home

Materials: large envelope, construction paper, crayons, markers, scissors, glue, pawns

Reproduce, color, cut out, and glue the "Going Home" game board to the front of a large envelope. Reproduce, color, laminate, then cut apart two sets of game cards. (These cards can also be used to play a game of Concentration.) To play: Shuffle and place the game cards on the table face down. In turn, each player picks a card and identifies the beginning sound letter that matches the picture. If correct, the player moves his or her pawn forward one space and the next player takes a turn. If incorrect, the player does not move forward. Play continues until all players reach The End. When all cards have been played, reshuffle and place the cards in a draw pile to continue play. Make additional picture word cards for children to practice identifying more beginning sound letters. Store cards and pawns inside the envelope.

MM2202 • Fun Fill-ins • ©2005 Monday Morning Books, Inc.

Going Home Game Board

Going Home

Start

The End

Yankee Doodle

Yankee Doodle went to town
Just to ride a pony.
He stuck a feather in his hat
and called it macaroni.

MM2202 • Fun Fill-ins • ©2005 Monday Morning Books, Inc.

Yankee Doodle

Yankee Doodle on a Pony

Reproduce a Yankee Doodle and pony pattern for children to color. Help each child cut out each pattern along the bold lines, then cut on the dotted line between Yankee Doodle's legs to mount him on the pony. Secure Yankee Doodle on the pony with a strip of tape. Glue a craft stick to the back of the pony to form a stick puppet.

Yankee Doodle

Yankee Doodle Headband
Measure and cut a construction paper headband for each child. Enlarge and reproduce a hat and feather pattern for children to color. Help each child cut out the patterns along the bold lines. Have children tape their feathers to their hats, then glue the hats to a headband. Tape or staple each child's headband. Option: Use real feathers.

MM2202 • Fun Fill-ins • ©2005 Monday Morning Books, Inc.

Yankee Doodle Story Board

Name _____

Yankee Doodle went to town

Just to ride a [   ] .

_____
Write the matching word here.

Read the words.
Cut out and glue a
picture in the
square.
Write the matching
word in the space
provided.

pig   pony   mouse

chicken   skateboard   goat

Yankee Doodle Story Board

Name _____

He stuck a [ ] in his hat

_____
Write the matching word here.

and called it macaroni.

Read the words. Cut out and glue a picture in the square. Write the matching word in the space provided.

feather

frog

peanut

chicken

cow

carrot

Yankee Doodle Writing Boards

Name _____

Name _____

Pony Race

Materials: large envelope, construction paper, crayons, markers, scissors, glue, pawns

Reproduce, color, cut out, and glue the "Find the Pony" game board to the front of a large envelope. Reproduce, color, laminate, then cut apart a set of game cards. (These cards can also be used to play a game of Concentration.) To play: Shuffle and place the game cards on the table face down. In turn, each player picks a card and identifies the beginning sound letter that matches the picture. If correct, the player moves his or her pawn forward one space and the next player takes a turn. If incorrect, the player does not move forward. Play continues until all players reach the pony. When all cards have been played, reshuffle and place the cards in a draw pile to continue play. Make additional picture word cards for children to practice identifying more beginning sound letters. Store cards and pawns inside the envelope.

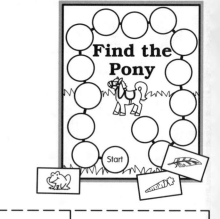

MM2202 • Fun Fill-ins • ©2005 Monday Morning Books, Inc.

Pony Race Game Board

Find the
Pony

Start

Beginning Word Cards

man	moon	children	earth
bed	horse	cow	shoe
box	pretzels	tub	turtles
brooms	elephants	horses	umbrellas

MM2202 • Fun Fill-ins • ©2005 Monday Morning Books, Inc.

Beginning Word Cards

pig

pail

up

water

down

crown

Jack

Jill

pigs

turtles

bees

alligators

kittens

cup

pillow

owl

Beginning Word Cards

pussycat	boat	honey	money
bunnies	elephants	puppies	ladybugs
carrots	pool	sandbox	umbrella
woman	children	soup	bread

 MM2202 • Fun Fill-ins • ©2005 Monday Morning Books, Inc.

Beginning Word Cards

bed	mailbox	ducks	cows
turtles	elephant	slide	pony
mouse	skateboard	goat	feather
peanut	carrot	heart	star

Picture Word Cards

MM2202 • Fun Fill-ins • ©2005 Monday Morning Books, Inc.

Picture Word Cards

Picture Word Cards

MM2202 • Fun Fill-ins • ©2005 Monday Morning Books, Inc.

Picture Word Cards

Rewards

Name

is an excellent reader.

Great Job!

Good Work!

MM2202 • Fun Fill-ins • ©2005 Monday Morning Books, Inc.

Rewards

Look Who's Doing Great Work!

I Can Read Beginning Words!

I'm a Beginning Word Reader

Mother Hubbard's Super Student Award

Rewards

Name

is an excellent reader.

Super Student

Great Job!

Good Work!

Look Who's Doing Great Work!

Beginning Word Reader

I Can Read Beginning Words!

MM2202 • Fun Fill-ins • ©2005 Monday Morning Books, Inc.